Jazz

This new edition published in 2005 by Smart Apple Media

2140 Howard Drive West, North Mankato, MN 56003

ISBN 1-58340-676-X

Design and Production by EvansDay Design

Photographs: pages 7, 17: Hulton-Deutsch Collection/
CORBIS; pages 8, 11, 21, 22: Bettmann/CORBIS;
page 10: Philip Gould/CORBIS; page 13: Kelly-Mooney
Photography/CORBIS; pages 18, 28: Lynn Goldsmith/CORBIS;
page 19: Robert Holmes/CORBIS; pages 23, 31: Derick A.
Thomas; Dat's Jazz/CORBIS; page 25: Dean Wong/CORBIS;
page 27: CORBIS

The Library of Congress has cataloged the earlier edition as follows:

Library of Congress Cataloging-in-Publication Data

Kirgiss, Crystal.

Jazz / by Crystal Kirgiss

p. cm. — (World of music)

Includes index.

Summary: Traces the origins of jazz music, examining its
unique rhythmic improvisation, instrumentation, scat
singing, changing styles, and prominent musicians.

ISBN 1-58340-043-5

1. Jazz—History and criticism—Juvenile literature. [1. Jazz.]

I. Title. II. Series: World of music (North Mankato, Minn.)

ML3506.K58   2002

781.65'09—dc21   99-31753

First paperback edition

2 4 6 8 9 7 5 3 1

Jazz

CRYSTAL KIRGISS

ON CHRISTMAS NIGHT, 1926, AT LEAST 500 party lovers decided to spend the evening in one of the many jazz clubs that lined a dark and narrow street in Chicago's entertainment district. There they could dance to jazz music and enjoy the wild atmosphere typical of the Roaring Twenties. On stage, a group of African-American men swayed to the drummer's beat, lost in the emotion of the music. Each of these musicians produced rhythms and harmonies that expressed everything from anger to joy to sorrow. Then, suddenly, police raided the club. In only minutes, most of the customers were arrested, though not for disturbing the peace or even for drinking illegally. Their crime was dancing. Some authorities thought it was out of control, and so—for that night at least—they outlawed jazz.

AN EARLY
History

 In January 1921, the town of Zion, Illinois, banned all jazz music, claiming that it was as bad for its citizens as tobacco and alcohol.

TIMES HAVE CHANGED A LOT SINCE 1926, and jazz has changed along with them, but it was a long process. The earliest roots of jazz were established in the South during the first half of the 19th century. Africans, abducted from their homeland and sold on the auction blocks as slaves in the United States, found some solace in music.

While working long days on their owners' plantations, slaves sang work songs, many of which expressed their anger, sorrow, and despair. They used field hollers and call-and-response songs to work steadily as a unit and to secretly communicate with neighboring slaves. They sang spirituals to keep alive their hope of freedom. When allowed to celebrate, they turned to emotion-filled singing and energetic dancing.

By the end of the American Civil War in 1865, blacks—using their voices and whatever homemade instruments they could create—had built a strong tradition of music that was highly rhythmic and deeply expressive.

EARLY 20TH-CENTURY
GUITARIST

These songs are part of the foundation of American folk music and an immediate ancestor of both blues and jazz.

In 1898, when army bands from the Spanish-American War disbanded, their instruments filled the pawnshops of the South, particularly in New Orleans. Jazz musicians began to add real instruments to their music-making.

KING OLIVER'S
CREOLE JAZZ BAND

FROM STORYVILLE
to Chicago

 In 1917, during World War I, Storyville was closed by the Secretary of the Navy, who worried that many of the businesses there were bad influences on young American sailors.

THAT SAME YEAR, THE STORYVILLE district was created in New Orleans. The streets were lined with cheap hotels, bars, and other disreputable businesses. Storyville musicians began playing some of the early forms of jazz. These included ragtime, very fast music full of bouncing rhythms often played on piano, and Dixieland, the two- and four-beat rhythmic songs of the street bands. Some of the greatest jazzmen of all time, including King Oliver and Louis Armstrong, got their start during these years.

Automobile and war supply factories in the North offered the promise of steady jobs, so

many people moved there from the South. Likewise, many jazzmen of New Orleans, with fewer places to perform at home, packed up and moved to Chicago and other cities east of there. Jazz slowly spread into the heartland of America, fitting in well with the fast pace of the 1920s.

By the middle of the Prohibition years, Chicago was filled with jazz clubs, and more than 40 top jazz musicians lived and performed there. Many other cities around the nation were home to jazz as well. Trom-

While in Los Angeles in 1921, trombonist Kid Ory became the first black jazz musician to make a recording. Two years later, Joseph "King" Oliver's Creole Jazz Band was the first black ensemble to be recorded.

bonist Kid Ory brought jazz to California before moving to Chicago. During the '20s, many jazz clubs were owned and run by gangsters such as Al Capone, and bootlegging—the sale of illegal liquor—was big business. Chicago and other large cities across the country became wild places during this time, known as The Golden Age of Jazz.

KID ORY

THE SOUNDS OF
New York

Many jazz historians feel that most of the truly great jazz singers of the past were women, including Bessie Smith, Sarah Vaughn, Ella Fitzgerald, and Billie Holiday. Instrumentalist Marylou Williams is known as the First Lady of Jazz.

WHEN THE STOCK MARKET CRASHED and the Great Depression hit America in the 1930s, many of Chicago's jazz clubs closed. As a result, a number of jazz musicians were forced to look elsewhere for work. Many of them went to New York City to play in such famous places as Birdland, Broadway, and Harlem's The Cotton Club. During this time, swing, or big-band, music was popular. Jazz groups of between 13 and 16 members played in dance halls and ballrooms all over the city. Often, two big bands engaged in "battles" from opposite sides of the dance floor, each trying to outplay and outsing the other.

At the forefront was the saxophone, which had become a key jazz instrument. The combination of this and other instruments in the big bands gave jazz two different sounds: "hot" and "sweet." The hot was expressed in the loud, blasting solos. The sweet came from the more mellow and sometimes muted sounds of the reeds (saxophone and clarinet) and brass (trombone and trumpet).

14

Jazz legend Duke Ellington composed more than 1,000 short songs, as well as various concertos for orchestra, concert pieces, jazz solos, religious compositions, and movie scores.

Some groups included a vocalist, singing either regular lyrics or scat—nonsensical syllables such as "bop-a-de-hop-sco-doo-bee-bop" or "bing-a-de-bajg-bajg-deedle-bo-bee-biddle." Louis Armstrong, the inventor of scat, claimed that it originated during one of his performances when he forgot the words and started making sounds that fit with the band.

All jazz soloists, whether instrumental or vocal, are known for bending the pitch of notes. This involves sliding up or down on a note, scooping into a note, or altering the pitch ever so slightly. This, along with rhythm syncopations and improvisation, is yet another one of the freedoms that jazz allows its performers.

SYNCOPATION &
Improvisation

Arthur Mitchell, the first black to become a principal dancer with the New York City Ballet, founded the Dance Theatre of Harlem in 1968 and went on to choreograph dances that combined jazz steps with classical ballet.

JAZZ RHYTHM IS FULL OF STRANGE twists and turns known as syncopation. Instead of an ordinary one-two-three-four beat, syncopation is full of bounces, skips, and hiccups. On top of that, the bounces, skips, and hiccups happen at different times on different instruments. While the drummer is bouncing on beats two and four, the bass player may be skipping on beats one and three, and the trumpet player may be sliding up and down the musical scale. In most music this would never work. But in jazz, it is the norm. This intricate balance of seemingly unrelated rhythms gives jazz its propulsive

character, seeming to invite listeners to tap their toes and snap their fingers.

Improvisation is the process of making up the music while playing. Though some jazz music is written out note for note so that each band member knows exactly what and when to play, much of it is only a basic sketch. The rhythm and chords are laid out, and within that framework, the soloist and other band members are free to play whatever suits their fancy. Only in jazz is a musician given this type of freedom.

SAXOPHONIST
DAVID SANBORN

Though the early musicians enjoyed performing before audiences, the real highlight for many of them was the after-hours jam session. When all of the club's patrons had gone, the musicians would pick up their instruments and start to improvise, creating new music for hours on end.

In December 1938, a new jazz club called Cafe Society opened in New York. Located in a white neighborhood, it was the first club to welcome both black and white customers through its doors.

19

A GROWING
Diversity

 During World War II, the government asked Americans to give up their old records so they could be melted down to make new ones, thus conserving the materials needed to produce them. Thousands of valuable jazz recordings were carried off in trucks to be destroyed.

DURING THE FIRST HALF OF THE 1900S, while jazz musicians were busy performing, jamming, and improving their skills, many American intellectuals ignored jazz as a serious musical art form. They considered it nothing more than pop culture. Many teens listened to it because their parents didn't approve of it. Some people looked down on jazz simply because it had been created by African-Americans. And some middle and upper-class African-Americans opposed it because it was a painful reminder of their culture's past history in slavery. Because it wasn't considered respectable, it was often

20

DIZZY GILLESPIE

CHARLIE PARKER

excluded from school curriculums. Jazz, however, was here to stay. In the 1940s and '50s, as public interest in jazz continued to grow, new styles emerged.

One style was bop, led by saxophonist Charlie Parker. This music had jumpy rhythms and was more flexible than big-band music. The beat made odd changes, extra notes were crowded into songs, and sometimes more than one melody was played at once. Bop groups usually included

22

five instruments: piano, bass, drums, saxophone or clarinet, and trumpet. Some bop greats were trumpeter Dizzy Gillespie and pianist Thelonius Monk. Bop never became as popular as swing, however, partly because it was not dancing music.

JAZZ SINGER
BETTY CARTER

Hoagy Carmichael was the composer of such jazz classics as "Lazy River," "Stardust," and "Georgia on My Mind." The legendary Bix Beiderbecke recorded Carmichael's first song, "Riverboat Shuffle."

AS JAZZ CONTINUED TO EVOLVE OVER the decades, another style to emerge was "cool" jazz, led by trumpeter Miles Davis. This music was mostly written down, not improvised. Some cool jazz groups played with great precision and intentionally tried to keep all feeling and emotion out of the music. California was a hotbed for cool jazz.

In response to the popularity of cool jazz, a new form of jazz called funk, or hard bop, was developed. Drummer Art Blakely and singer/pianist Ray Charles, the leaders of this style, wanted to give back to jazz the energy and soul that had been lost in the swing and cool jazz eras.

In 1960, saxophonist Ornette Coleman
and trumpeter Don Cherry recorded *Free
Jazz*, a 36.5-minute album featuring one
single improvised song. The rhythms were
undefined, and the melodies included
strange new sounds. Instruments seemed to
be playing against each other instead of with
each other. Though jazz had always been
more free than other types of music, this
avant-garde style was too free and loose for
many listeners. Coleman was once even at-
tacked by some men who were angered by
the unconventional way he played.

During jam sessions, soloists would sometimes have "cutting" contests. The goal was to outplay one another, both in skill and creativity, and "cut" the other person down to size.

MORE CONVENTIONAL, YET VERY DIF-ferent from what had been done previously, a new sound called "fusion" was embraced by jazz listeners during the 1970s. Chick Corea and Herbie Hancock, both keyboardists, first introduced the world to fusion, a mixture of jazz and rock that results when jazz musicians incorporate popular rock elements in their music or rock musicians include jazz elements. The bands Blood, Sweat & Tears and Chicago were both commercially successful fusion groups that featured jazz horn sections.

HERBIE HANCOCK

WYNTON MARSALIS

Jazz is now entering its second century, but even after so many years, it is still difficult to give jazz a precise definition. It has constantly changed and evolved, expanding to include other musical genres and being absorbed by them as well. Most music historians agree that by the 1980s, jazz had become a firmly established and accepted musical form. Though not as widely

In 1997, Wynton Marsalis was awarded the Pulitzer Prize in music—the first Pulitzer ever given for jazz.

heard as country, rock, and pop, jazz has carved its own permanent niche in the world of music.

Instead of dancing, many jazz fans prefer to sit and listen to the music. They admire the musicians' expertise and appreciate the rhythms and harmonies and breathtaking solos for what they really are—highly practiced artistic creations. Those who like to dance can still do so as well, as swing—an earlier jazz style—has made a comeback with both musicians and dancers.

Many New Age composers, such as pianist George Winston, draw from the unpredictable improvisation traditions of jazz music to create what they call "audio environments" rather than structured songs.

TODAY, MOST CONTEMPORARY JAZZ musicians are highly trained in performance, composition, and theory. A new group of performers, including Wynton Marsalis, his brother Brandon, Harry Connick Jr., and Tom Harrell, have brought jazz to the forefront of the music scene, playing both traditional and innovative styles.

Jazz bands have appeared regularly on such diverse shows as *Mister Rogers' Neighborhood* and *Saturday Night Live*. Both *Late Night with David Letterman* and *The Tonight Show* have featured jazz groups that define the show as much as the host and guests.

From the high school jazz band to the night club jazz ensemble, the world of rhythmic improvisation continues to beckon a broad spectrum of musicians. Now in its second century, it is clear that jazz is not so much a kind of music as it is an approach to playing music. As jazz great Fats Waller once said, "If you have to explain jazz, then you don't know what it is."